PEARSON EDEXCEL INTERNATIONAL AS/A LEVEL

CHEMISTRY

Lab Book

Published by Pearson Education Limited, 80 Strand, London, WC2R 0RL.

www.pearsonglobalschools.com

Copies of official specifications for all Pearson Edexcel qualifications may be found on the website: https://qualifications.pearson.com

Text © Pearson Education Limited 2018
Designed by Tech-Set Ltd, Gateshead, UK
Edited by Katharine Godfrey Smith, Helen Payne and Stephanie White
Typeset by Tech-Set Ltd, Gateshead, UK
Original illustrations © Pearson Education Limited 2018
Cover design © Pearson Education Limited 2018

The rights of Carl Howe and Nigel Saunders to be identified as authors of this work have been asserted by them in accordance with the Copyright, Designs and Patents Act 1988.

The Publishers would like to thank Mark Woods for his contributions to the text.

First published 2018

25 24 23
IMP 14

British Library Cataloguing in Publication Data
A catalogue record for this book is available from the British Library
ISBN 978 1 292 24471 6

Printed in Slovakia by Neografia

Acknowledgements
All artwork © Pearson Education Limited 2018

A note from the publishers:
While the Publishers have made every attempt to ensure that advice on the qualification and its assessment is accurate, the official specification and associated assessment guidance materials are the only authoritative source of information and should always be referred to for definitive guidance. Pearson examiners have not contributed to any sections in this resource relevant to examination papers for which they have responsibility. Examiners will not use this resource as a source of material for any assessment set by Pearson.

Neither Pearson, Edexcel nor the authors take responsibility for the safety of any activity. Before doing any practical activity you are legally required to carry out your own risk assessment. In particular, any local rules issued by your employer must be obeyed, regardless of what is recommended in this resource. Where students are required to write their own risk assessments they must always be checked by the teacher and revised, as necessary, to cover any issues the students may have overlooked. The teacher should always have the final control as to how the practical is conducted.

CONTENTS

Practical work is central to the study of chemistry. The International Advanced Subsidiary/Advanced Level (IAS/IAL) specification includes 16 core practical activities that link theoretical knowledge and understanding to practical scenarios. By completing the core practical activities, you will learn to:

- follow and interpret experimental instructions, covering a range of laboratory exercises throughout the course, with minimal help from your teacher
- manipulate apparatus, use chemicals, carry out all common laboratory procedures and use data logging (where appropriate)
- work sensibly and safely in the laboratory, paying due regard to health and safety requirements
- gain accurate and consistent results in quantitative exercises, and make the most of the expected observations in qualitative exercises.

By the end of this course, you should be able to use a variety of apparatus and techniques to:

- design and carry out both the core practical activities and your own investigations
- collect data that can be analysed
- use data to draw valid conclusions.

Your knowledge and understanding of practical skills and activities will be assessed in all examination papers.

- Papers 1 and 2 (IAS), and 4 and 5 (IAL) will include questions based on practical activities, including novel scenarios
- Papers 3 (IAS) and 6 (IAL) will test your ability to plan practical work, including risk management and selection of apparatus.

Assessment for the Practical Skills Papers 3 and 6 will focus on four main areas:

- independent thinking
- use and application of scientific methods and practices
- numeracy and the application of mathematical concepts
- use of apparatus and equipment.

The ways in which you can demonstrate these practical skills are outlined in the tables on pages 4 and 5. You may wish to tick off each element as you gain confidence.

You will find answers and maths skills required for the practicals in the back of the book.

Practical skills	Core Practical							
Independent thinking in a practical context	1	2	3	4	5	6	7	8
Solve problems set in a practical context								
Apply scientific knowledge to practical contexts								
Use and application of scientific methods and practices	1	2	3	4	5	6	7	8
Identify and state how to control variables to improve experimental validity								
Present data in appropriate ways								
Evaluate results and draw conclusions								
Appreciate measurement uncertainties and errors								
Comment on the method for an experiment								
Numeracy and the application of mathematical concepts in a practical context	1	2	3	4	5	6	7	8
Plot and interpret graphs								
Process and analyse data using appropriate mathematical skills								
Use appropriate numbers of significant figures based on the experimental data								
Consider the accuracy and precision of data								
Use of apparatus and equipment	1	2	3	4	5	6	7	8
Recognise a range of laboratory apparatus and select appropriate apparatus for a particular scenario								
Understand how to use a range of apparatus and techniques appropriate to the knowledge and understanding included in the specification								
Consider the range and resolution of apparatus								
Identify health and safety issues and discuss how these may be dealt with								

Practical skills	Core Practical									
Independent thinking in a practical context	**9a**	**9b**	**10**	**11**	**12**	**13a**	**13b**	**14**	**15**	**16**
Solve problems set in a practical context										
Apply scientific knowledge to practical contexts										
Use and application of scientific methods and practices	**9a**	**9b**	**10**	**11**	**12**	**13a**	**13b**	**14**	**15**	**16**
Identify and state how to control variables to improve experimental validity										
Present data in appropriate ways										
Evaluate results and draw conclusions										
Appreciate measurement uncertainties and errors										
Comment on the method for an experiment										
Numeracy and the application of mathematical concepts in a practical context	**9a**	**9b**	**10**	**11**	**12**	**13a**	**13b**	**14**	**15**	**16**
Plot and interpret graphs										
Process and analyse data using appropriate mathematical skills										
Use appropriate numbers of significant figures based on the experimental data										
Consider the accuracy and precision of data										
Use of apparatus and equipment	**9a**	**9b**	**10**	**11**	**12**	**13a**	**13b**	**14**	**15**	**16**
Recognise a range of laboratory apparatus and select appropriate apparatus for a particular scenario										
Understand how to use a range of apparatus and techniques appropriate to the knowledge and understanding included in the specification										
Consider the range and resolution of apparatus										
Identify health and safety issues and discuss how these may be dealt with										

Procedure

1 Set up the apparatus to capture and measure gas evolved from a reaction in the boiling tube.

2 Place 30 cm³ of 1 mol dm⁻³ ethanoic acid in the boiling tube.

3 Place approximately 0.05 g of calcium carbonate in a test tube. Weigh the test tube and its contents accurately.

4 Remove the bung from the boiling tube and tip the calcium carbonate into the boiling tube. Quickly replace the bung in the boiling tube.

5 Once the reaction is over, measure the volume of gas produced.

6 Reweigh the test tube that contained the calcium carbonate.

7 Repeat the experiment six more times, increasing the mass of calcium carbonate by about 0.05 g each time. Do not exceed 0.40 g of calcium carbonate.

Learning tips

- Ensure that points plotted on a graph take up more than half the available space on each scale. Axes must occupy at least half of the space on the graph paper.
- Keep scales simple: one large square as 5 or 10 or 20 is ideal. A scale where one large square represents 3 or 7 units (or similar) is very difficult to plot on, and this often leads to errors.
- Always consider whether the graph line should go through the origin.
- Straight lines should be drawn with the aid of a ruler long enough to cover the full length of the line.

Objectives

- To find the volume of one mole of carbon dioxide gas

Equipment

- boiling tube
- stand and clamp
- bung fitted with delivery tube to fit boiling tube
- water bath for gas collection
- 100 cm³ measuring cylinder
- 50 cm³ measuring cylinder
- test tube
- mass balance (2 d.p.)
- 1 mol dm⁻³ ethanoic acid
- powdered calcium carbonate

⚠ Safety

- Wear eye protection.
- Remove the bung if the delivery tube gets blocked, clear the blockage and repeat the procedure from the start.
- Avoid skin contact with the ethanoic acid, especially if the skin is broken or sensitive.

Results (Use this space to record your results.)

Analysis of results

1 Plot a graph of mass of calcium carbonate (on the x-axis) against volume of carbon dioxide collected (on the y-axis). Draw a straight line of best fit – this line must pass through the origin.

Use your graph to find the volume of carbon dioxide that would be made from 0.25 g of calcium carbonate.

In this reaction, one mole of calcium carbonate makes one mole of carbon dioxide. Calculate the number of moles of calcium carbonate in 0.25 g and hence calculate the volume of one mole of carbon dioxide gas in dm^3.

Questions

1 Write a chemical equation for the reaction between ethanoic acid, CH_3COOH, and calcium carbonate.

2 Why is it more accurate to find the mass of the calcium carbonate used by weighing the test tube containing the calcium carbonate and then reweighing the test tube after the calcium carbonate has been tipped out, rather than by weighing the empty test tube at the start?

....

....

....

....

....

3 Identify the major source of error caused by the procedure used here.

....

....

....

4 What change to the procedure/apparatus could you make to eradicate this error?

....

....

....

....

5 Carry out two calculations to show that the ethanoic acid was in excess in all experimental runs.

Procedure

Place approximately 3 g of solid potassium carbonate in a test tube. Accurately weigh the test tube and its contents.

Use a burette to dispense 30 cm^3 of 2 mol dm^{-3} hydrochloric acid into a polystyrene cup, which is supported in a beaker.

Measure the temperature of the acid.

Gradually add potassium carbonate to the acid, stirring all the time and monitoring the temperature of the acid.

Reweigh the empty test tube.

Repeat steps 1–5 using approximately 3.5 g of potassium hydrogencarbonate instead of the potassium carbonate. This time, record the lowest temperature reached.

Results (Use this space to record your results.)

Mass of test tube with potassium carbonate/g	
Mass of test tube after emptying out potassium carbonate/g	
Mass of potassium carbonate used/g	
Start temperature/°C	
Highest temperature/°C	
Temperature change/°C	

Mass of test tube with potassium hydrogencarbonate/g	
Mass of test tube after emptying out potassium hydrogencarbonate/g	
Mass of potassium hydrogencarbonate used/g	
Start temperature/°C	
Lowest temperature/°C	
Temperature change/°C	

Objectives

- To calculate the molar enthalpy change for two reactions and use Hess's Law to determine the enthalpy change for the reactions

Equipment

- two test tubes
- 2 mol dm^{-3} dilute hydrochloric acid
- solid potassium carbonate
- solid potassium hydrogencarbonate
- thermometer able to read up to 50 °C or more
- polystyrene cup
- 250 cm^3 or 400 cm^3 beaker
- burette, clamp and stand
- stirring rod
- mass balance (2 d.p.)
- spatula

⚠ Safety

- Wear eye protection.
- Avoid skin contact with the reactants and products.

Learning tips

- You can assume that the heat capacity of the final solution is the same as the heat capacity of water. The volume of water produced in the reaction is so small it can be ignored.
- For exothermic reactions, the enthalpy change, $\triangle H$, is negative.
- Be careful to use equals signs correctly. It is very easy to end up stating that a negative number equals a positive number.

Analysis of results

1 The equations for the reactions occurring are:

reaction 1: $K_2CO_3(s) + 2HCl(aq) \rightarrow 2KCl(aq) + CO_2(g) + H_2O(l)$

reaction 2: $KHCO_3(s) + HCl(aq) \rightarrow KCl(aq) + CO_2(g) + H_2O(l)$

Calculate the energy change for each reaction in J. (The specific heat capacity of water is $4.2\,J\,g^{-1}\,°C^{-1}$.)

2 Calculate the enthalpy change, $\triangle H$, for each reaction in $kJ\,mol^{-1}$.
Assume that the hydrochloric acid is in excess.

3 Use your results to calculate the enthalpy change for the thermal decomposition of potassium hydrogencarbonate:

reaction 3: $2KHCO_3(s) \rightarrow K_2CO_3(s) + CO_2(g) + H_2O(l)$

Questions

Why is it not possible to measure the enthalpy change for the decomposition of potassium hydrogencarbonate directly?

....

....

....

....

....

Show that the hydrochloric acid is in excess in both reactions.

3 Draw an energy level diagram for each reaction: 1, 2 and 3.

4 Explain why the reactions are conducted in a polystyrene cup rather than a glass beaker.

....

....

....

....

....

Procedure

Wash out the 250 cm³ volumetric flask with distilled water.

Use the pipette to transfer 25.0 cm³ of the hydrochloric acid solution into the volumetric flask. Use distilled water to make the solution up to the mark.

Prepare your apparatus for the titration. The burette should contain the sodium hydroxide solution (previously standardised) and the conical flask should contain the dilute hydrochloric acid solution.

Pour a 25.0 cm³ aliquot of the diluted hydrochloric acid into the conical flask. Use phenolphthalein as the indicator.

Titrate the contents of the flask against the sodium hydroxide solution. Record all burette readings to the nearest 0.05 cm³.

The end point of this titration is indicated by the contents of the flask becoming pale pink. Continued swirling will cause the pink colour to fade and disappear. If the pink colour persists for 5 seconds or more, the end point has been reached.

Conduct further titrations until you have two concordant titres.

Ask your teacher or a technician to check one of your burette readings.

Record your results in the table below.

Learning tips

Do not include your rough titration when calculating your mean.

Give all burette readings to the nearest 0.05 cm³.

When you scale up to find the number of moles in the full volume of solution in the volumetric flask, use this equation:

number of moles in full volume

$$= \frac{\text{full volume} \times \text{number of moles in aliquot volume}}{\text{aliquot volume in which you know the number of moles}}$$

Objectives

- To find the concentration of a solution of hydrochloric acid

Equipment

- burette, clamp and stand
- sodium hydroxide solution (approximately 0.08 dm³, previously standardised)
- bench hydrochloric acid (approximately 1 mol dm⁻³)
- phenolphthalein
- 250 cm³ conical flask
- 25 cm³ volumetric pipette plus safety filler
- 100 cm³ beakers for transfer of solutions
- funnel for filling burette
- 250 cm³ beaker
- 250 cm³ volumetric flask

⚠ Safety

- Wear eye protection. Goggles are preferred as sodium hydroxide is particularly hazardous to the eyes.
- Avoid skin contact with the acid, alkali and indicator.
- Always use a pipette filler; never use your mouth to suck the liquid up.
- Take care when clamping and filling the burette that it does not crack or topple over.

Results (Use this space to record your results.)

	Rough	Trial 1	Trial 2	Trial 3	Trial 4
Final burette reading/cm³					
Initial burette reading/cm³					
Titre/cm³					
Concordant (Y/N)					

Analysis of results

1   Calculate the mean titre using your two concordant results.

2   Calculate the number of moles of sodium hydroxide that were contained in your mean titre.

3   Calculate the number of moles of hydrochloric acid that were contained in the full $250\,cm^3$ of diluted hydrochloric acid.

4   Calculate the concentration of the original solution of hydrochloric acid.

Questions

Write a chemical equation for the reaction of hydrochloric acid with sodium hydroxide.

The pink colour seen at the end point fades because the excess sodium hydroxide reacts with carbon dioxide in the air. This reaction produces sodium carbonate.

a   Write an equation for the reaction of sodium hydroxide with carbon dioxide.

b   When sodium hydroxide solution is stored, it reacts with carbon dioxide in the air.

   i   How will this change the concentration of the sodium hydroxide solution?

....

....

   ii How will this affect the volume of sodium hydroxide solution required to reach the end point in the titration? Explain your answer.

....

....

....

....

....

....

....

....

....

....

Explain why it is better to have a titre of around $25 \, cm^3$ than a titre of around $10 \, cm^3$.

....

....

....

....

....

CORE PRACTICAL 4:
PREPARATION OF A STANDARD SOLUTION FROM A SOLID ACID AND ITS USE TO FIND
THE CONCENTRATION OF A SOLUTION OF SODIUM HYDROXIDE

SPECIFICAT
REFERENC

8.23

Procedure

1 Weigh an empty test tube. Scoop approximately 2.5 g of sulfamic acid into the test tube.

2 Accurately reweigh the test tube and its contents.

3 Dissolve the sulfamic acid in approximately 100 cm³ of water in a beaker.

4 Transfer the solution, including the washings, to a 250 cm³ volumetric flask and use distilled water to make up the solution to the mark.

5 Prepare your apparatus for the titration. The burette will contain the acid and the conical flask will contain the sodium hydroxide solution.

6 Pour a 25.0 cm³ aliquot of sodium hydroxide solution of unknown concentration into the 250 cm³ conical flask.

7 Use methyl orange as the indicator.

8 Titrate the contents of the flask against the sulfamic acid solution you prepared. Burette readings should be to the nearest 0.05 cm³.

9 Conduct further titrations until you have two concordant titres.

10 Record your results in the table below.

Learning tips

- Indicators are very dilute weak acids. The more indicator you add, the less accurate your titration result will be.

- When conducting a titration, use distilled water to wash down the inside of the conical flask from time to time.

- When you scale up to find the number of moles in the full volume of solution in the volumetric flask, use this equation:

number of moles in full volume

$$= \frac{\text{full volume} \times \text{number of moles in aliquot volume}}{\text{aliquot volume in which you know the number of moles}}$$

Objectives

- To make a solution of a known concentration of acid and use it to find the concentration of a solution of sodium hydroxide

Equipment

- burette, clamp and stand
- solid sulfamic acid
- sodium hydroxide solution of unknown concentration
- methyl orange indicator
- 250 cm³ conical flask
- 25 cm³ volumetric pipette plus safety filler
- 100 cm³ beaker for transfer of solutions
- funnel for filling burette
- 250 cm³ beaker
- 250 cm³ volumetric flask
- mass balance (2 d.p.)

⚠ Safety

- Wear eye protection. Goggles are preferred as sodium hydroxide is particularly hazardous to the eyes.
- Avoid skin contact with sulfamic acid and sodium hydroxide.
- Take care when clamping and filling the burette that it does not crack or topple over.

Results (Use this space to record your results.)

		Mass of sulfamic acid =		g		
	Rough	Trial 1	Trial 2	Trial 3	Trial 4
Final burette reading/cm³						
Initial burette reading/cm³						
Titre/cm³						
Concordant (Y/N)						

RE PRACTICAL 4:
EPARATION OF A STANDARD SOLUTION FROM A SOLID ACID AND ITS USE TO FIND
CONCENTRATION OF A SOLUTION OF SODIUM HYDROXIDE

SPECIFICATION
REFERENCE

8.23

nalysis of results

Calculate the concentration of your sulfamic acid solution. The M_r of sulfamic acid is 97.1.

Calculate the mean titre using your concordant results.

Calculate the number of moles of sulfamic acid in your mean titre.

Sulfamic acid is a monoprotic acid. This means that one mole of sulfamic acid will react exactly with one mole of sodium hydroxide. Calculate the concentration of the sodium hydroxide solution used.

CORE PRACTICAL 4:
PREPARATION OF A STANDARD SOLUTION FROM A SOLID ACID AND ITS USE TO FIND
THE CONCENTRATION OF A SOLUTION OF SODIUM HYDROXIDE

SPECIFICAT
REFERENCE

8.23

Questions

1 A 250 cm³ volumetric flask has an accuracy of ±0.6 cm³. Calculate the percentage uncertainty in the volume of the sulfamic acid solution in the volumetric flask.

2 Each burette reading is accurate to ±0.05 cm³. Calculate the percentage uncertainty in one of your titres.

3 Why should the pipette be rinsed with the sodium hydroxide solution after it has been washed with water?

....

....

....

....

4 Why is there no need to dry the conical flask after washing it out between trials?

....

....

....

....

5 Identify another indicator you could use in this titration, and state the colour change you would see at the end point.

....

....

....

Procedure

Part 1

Set up a water bath by filling the 250 cm³ beaker up to the three-quarters mark with water at around 50 °C.

Take three test tubes and add 5 cm³ of ethanol to each one.

Add four drops of 1-iodobutane to the first tube, four drops of 1-bromobutane to the second tube and four drops of 1-chlorobutane to the third tube. Label the tubes.

Loosely place a bung in each test tube and place the test tubes in the water bath.

Take three clean test tubes and pour 5 cm³ of silver nitrate solution into each one. Then place the test tubes in the water bath.

When the halogenoalkane–ethanol solutions have reached the temperature of the water bath, add one test tube of silver nitrate solution to one of the halogenoalkane–ethanol solutions and replace the bung. At the same time, start the stop clock.

Measure the time taken for a precipitate to appear. As soon as the solution becomes cloudy, stop the stop clock.

Repeat steps **6** and **7** for the other two halogenoalkanes.

Part 2

Repeat Part 1 using 1-bromobutane, 2-bromobutane and 2-bromo-2-methylpropane instead of the other halogenoalkanes.

Results (Use this space to record your results.)

Objectives

- To investigate the relative rates of hydrolysis of primary, secondary and tertiary halogenoalkanes and of chloro-, bromo- and iodoalkanes

Equipment

- 250 cm³ beaker
- 12 test tubes with bungs
- 1-chlorobutane
- 1-bromobutane
- 1-iodobutane
- 2-bromobutane
- 2-bromo-2-methylpropane
- 0.05 mol dm⁻³ silver nitrate solution
- 15 cm³ ethanol
- dropping pipettes
- two 10 cm³ measuring cylinders
- stop clock
- labels for test tubes
- kettle

⚠ Safety

- Wear eye protection.
- Avoid skin contact with the reactants.
- There must be no naked flames in the vicinity as ethanol and halogenoalkanes are highly flammable.
- The laboratory needs to be well ventilated to prevent the inhalation of fumes.

Learning tips

- The hydrolysis of halogenoalkanes is a nucleophilic substitution reaction.
- In this investigation, the nucleophile is water.
- NaOH can be used instead of water to hydrolyse the halogenoalkanes but then any excess NaOH must be neutralised by HNO_3 before the $AgNO_3$ is added. Otherwise a precipitate of Ag_2O will form.

Analysis of results

1 Describe the pattern shown in your results for Part 1.

2 Describe the pattern shown in your results for Part 2.

Questions

1 Write an equation for the reaction of 1-bromobutane with water.

2 In these reactions, a precipitate forms. Identify the precipitate formed when the halogenoalkane is 1-iodobutane.

Explain why ethanol is used in these reactions.

....

....

....

....

Explain why water is able to act as a nucleophile.

....

....

....

Explain why water is used as the nucleophile rather than hydroxide ions.

....

....

....

Draw skeletal formulae for each of the halogenoalkanes used in this investigation (there are five of them). Classify each halogenoalkane as primary, secondary or tertiary.

Procedure

1 Pour 10 cm³ of 2-methylpropan-2-ol and 35 cm³ of concentrated hydrochloric acid into a large conical flask. Very gently swirl the contents of the flask.

2 Place the bung in the mouth of the flask. Gently swirl again, then remove the bung to release the pressure.

3 Continue swirling the mixture with the bung fitted, and then releasing the pressure, for around 20 minutes. You should see two layers in the flask. The upper layer is the crude product.

4 Add approximately 6 g of powdered anhydrous calcium chloride to the flask and swirl until it has dissolved. This will ensure that any unreacted alcohol is in the lower aqueous layer.

5 Transfer the reaction mixture to a separating funnel. Allow the mixture to settle into the two layers. Run off and discard the lower layer. Retain the upper organic layer in the separating funnel.

6 Add approximately 20 cm³ of sodium hydrogencarbonate solution to the separating funnel. Swirl the funnel. The production of carbon dioxide will cause the pressure to increase; remove the bung at frequent intervals to release this pressure. Run off and discard the lower aqueous layer.

7 Repeat the washing with sodium hydrogencarbonate solution, shake the separating funnel, and release the carbon dioxide gas produced, at frequent intervals.

8 Run off and discard the lower layer. Ensure none of the aqueous layer remains in the tap.

9 Run off the organic layer into a small conical flask. Add a full spatula of anhydrous sodium sulfate. Place the bung in the flask and swirl the contents to mix. Leave the mixture until the liquid looks completely clear, swirling occasionally.

10 Decant the organic liquid into a 50 cm³ pear-shaped (or round-bottomed) flask.

11 Set up the flask for distillation.

12 Collect the fraction boiling between 50 °C and 52 °C.

13 Place your pure product in a labelled sample tube.

14 Carry out the test described in the 'Analysis' section of this practical.

Learning tips

- The OH group in an alcohol can be replaced by a halogen. As well as the method used here to chlorinate an alcohol, PCl_5 can be used to make a chloroalkane. HBr (which is made in situ) can be used to make a bromoalkane. Red phosphorus with iodine can be used to make an iodoalkane.
- You can check the purity of a substance by measuring its boiling temperature.

Objectives

- To produce and purify a sample of 2-chloro-2-methylpropane

Equipment

- 250 cm³ conical flask with bung
- 100 cm³ (or larger) separating funnel with bung
- 250 cm³ beaker for liquid run off from separating funnel
- filter funnel to fit separating funnel
- apparatus for distillation with 50 cm³ pear-shaped (or round-bottomed) flask and thermometer able to read up to 100 °C
- 25 cm³ and 100 cm³ measuring cylinders
- 2-methylpropan-2-ol
- 0.1 mol dm⁻³ sodium hydrogencarbonate solution
- 6 g powdered anhydrous calcium chloride
- anhydrous sodium sulfate
- small conical flasks with bung
- sample tube
- 0.05 mol dm⁻³ silver nitrate solution
- dilute (0.5 mol dm⁻³) sodium hydroxide solution
- dilute (0.1 mol dm⁻³) nitric aci
- 70 cm³ concentrated hydrochloric acid
- test tubes
- spatulas
- 5 cm³ ethanol
- Bunsen burner
- beaker for water bath

⚠ Safety

- This procedure requires the use of a working fume cupboard.
- Wear eye protection. Goggles are preferred.
- Avoid skin contact with the reactants and products. Wear gloves.
- Avoid inhaling vapours.
- The product of the distillation process is flammable.
- The fumes from the concentrated hydrochloric acid are toxic and corrosive and must not be inhaled, especially by anyone with a respiratory problem.

esults (Use this space to record your results.)

nalysis of results

erform the following test on the distillate.

Place a few drops of the distillate in a test tube.

Add $5\,cm^3$ of ethanol and $1\,cm^3$ of aqueous sodium hydroxide to the test tube.

Warm the mixture in a water bath.

Add excess nitric acid to the mixture followed by a few drops of silver nitrate solution.

escribe what you see.

Questions

1 Write an equation for the reaction of 2-methylpropan-2-ol with concentrated hydrochloric acid.

2 What is removed from the crude product when it is shaken with sodium hydrogencarbonate solution? Write an equation for any reaction that occurs.

3 2-methylpropan-2-ol has a boiling temperature of 82 °C and is soluble in water. 2-chloro-2-methylpropane has a boiling temperature of 51 °C and is insoluble in water. Explain these differences.

Procedure 1a: Making propanal

Wear protective gloves when handling acidified potassium dichromate solution. Carefully add $20\,cm^3$ of acidified potassium dichromate solution to a $50\,cm^3$ pear-shaped flask. Cool the flask in an ice-water bath.

Set the flask up for distillation, keeping it in the ice-water bath.

Place a few anti-bumping granules into the pear-shaped flask.

Measure $1.5\,cm^3$ of propan-1-ol into a measuring cylinder and add $5\,cm^3$ of distilled water to this.

Using a pipette, add the propan-1-ol solution prepared in step 4, a few drops at a time, into the pear-shaped flask. Allow the reaction to subside after each addition before adding more.

When all the propan-1-ol solution has been added, remove the ice-water bath and allow the pear-shaped flask to warm to room temperature (approximately 5 minutes).

Light a burner under the flask and heat very gently with a small flame.

Collect $3-4\,cm^3$ of clear, colourless liquid in a test tube which is immersed in cold water in a beaker. The distillate needs to be the amount specified as there are several tests to be carried out to confirm that it is propanal.

Procedure 1b: Testing for propanal

Silver mirror test

1 Prepare a sample of Tollens' reagent by adding 5 drops of sodium hydroxide solution to $2\,cm^3$ of silver nitrate solution in a test tube.

2 Add just enough dilute ammonia solution to this test tube so that the brown precipitate dissolves completely. Using a water bath, gently warm this test tube.

3 Add 10 drops of the distillate obtained in step 8. If propanal has been produced, a silver mirror will appear on the walls of the test tube.

Magnesium ribbon

1 Add a small piece (1 cm length) of magnesium ribbon to the distillate.

2 Observe any reaction. Propanal does not react with magnesium, so nothing should be seen happening in the test tube.

Sodium hydrogencarbonate

1 Add a spatula of sodium hydrogencarbonate to the distillate in a test tube.

2 Observe any reaction. Propanal does not produce any effervescence.

Fehling's solution

1 Add $1\,cm^3$ Fehling's solution to $1\,cm^3$ of the distillate in a test tube.

2 Place the test tube into a beaker of hot water. A colour change to reddish-brown indicates propanal is present.

Learning tips

You should understand when to use distillation conditions or reflux conditions in the oxidation of alcohols.

You should be able to write equations for the oxidation of primary and secondary alcohols.

You should know that carboxylic acids are weak acids and that they show the typical reactions of acids. You should be able to write equations for these reactions.

Objectives

- To oxidise propan-1-ol to produce propanal by heating and distillation
- To oxidise propan-1-ol to produce propanoic acid by heating under reflux and distillation

Equipment

- simple distillation apparatus OR Quickfit® apparatus
- acidified potassium dichromate(VI)
- propan-1-ol
- distilled water
- teat pipette
- Bunsen burner or micro burner
- stand and clamp
- measuring cylinders
- anti-bumping granules
- test tubes
- spatula
- thermometer
- $10\,cm^3$ beakers
- $0.05\,mol\,dm^{-3}$ silver nitrate solution
- $2\,mol\,dm^{-3}$ dilute ammonia solution
- $2\,mol\,dm^{-3}$ sodium hydroxide solution
- small pieces of magnesium ribbon
- sodium hydrogencarbonate
- Fehling's solution

⚠ Safety

- Wear goggles and chemical-resistant gloves.
- Propan-1-ol and propanal are flammable.
- Avoid skin contact with the reactants and products.

Draw a diagram showing the distillation apparatus.

Results (Use this space to record your results.)

rocedure 2a: Making propanoic acid

Wear protective gloves when handling acidified potassium dichromate solution. Carefully add $20\,cm^3$ of acidified potassium dichromate solution to a $50\,cm^3$ pear-shaped flask. Cool the flask in an ice-water bath.

Set the flask up for reflux, keeping it in the ice-water bath.

Place a few anti-bumping granules into the pear-shaped flask.

Measure out $1.5\,cm^3$ of propan-1-ol into a measuring cylinder and add $5\,cm^3$ of distilled water to this.

Using a pipette, add the propan-1-ol solution prepared in step 4, a few drops at a time, down the reflux condenser. This must be done slowly. Allow the reaction to subside after each addition before adding more.

When all the propan-1-ol has been added, remove the ice-water bath and allow the pear-shaped flask to warm to room temperature (approximately 5 minutes).

Light a burner under the flask and heat gently under reflux with a small flame for 30 minutes.

Distil your product using the distillation apparatus. Collect $3–4\,cm^3$ of clear, colourless liquid in a test tube which is immersed in cold water in a beaker. The distillate needs to be the amount specified as there are several tests to be carried out to confirm that it is propanoic acid.

ocedure 2b: Testing for propanoic acid

Silver mirror test

1 Prepare a sample of Tollens' reagent by adding 5 drops of sodium hydroxide solution to $2\,cm^3$ of silver nitrate solution in a test tube.

2 Add just enough dilute ammonia solution to this test tube so that the brown precipitate dissolves completely. Using a water bath, gently warm this test tube.

3 Add 10 drops of the distillate obtained in step 8. If propanoic acid has been produced a silver mirror will **not** appear on the walls of the test tube.

Magnesium ribbon

1 Add a small piece (1 cm length) of magnesium ribbon to the distillate.

2 Observe any reaction. Propanoic acid does react with magnesium, so some effervescence should be seen in the test tube.

Sodium hydrogencarbonate

1 Add a spatula of sodium hydrogencarbonate to the distillate in a test tube.

2 Observe any reaction. Propanoic acid does produce effervescence and this should be clearly seen.

Fehling's solution

1 Add $1\,cm^3$ Fehling's solution to $1\,cm^3$ of the distillate in a test tube.

2 Place the test tube into a beaker of hot water. Propanoic acid does not cause Fehling's solution to change colour.

Draw a diagram showing the apparatus for the reflux stage.

Results (Use this space to record your results.)

Questions

What is meant by the term 'reflux'?

....

....

....

In step 5 in both experiments, why do you have to add the propan-1-ol solution slowly?

....

....

Why are anti-bumping granules added to the reaction mixture?

....

....

Why should the water enter the condenser at the bottom?

....

....

Why does the test tube for collecting the distillate need to be surrounded by cold water?

....

....

Write an equation for the oxidation of propan-1-ol to propanal. Use [O] to represent the oxidising agent.

Write an equation for the oxidation of propan-1-ol to propanoic acid. Use [O] to represent the oxidising agent.

Draw fully displayed formulae for propan-1-ol, propanal and propanoic acid.

9 Why can propanal only be obtained without the reflux step?

....

....

....

10 Propan-1-ol is a primary alcohol. Research what happens when secondary and tertiary alcohols are oxidised. Some space has been left to allow you to draw any displayed formula diagrams that you found useful.

....

....

....

....

....

....

....

....

....

....

....

....

....

....

....

....

....

Procedure

Part 1

Perform the following tests on each of the organic liquids A, B and C. Record your observations in the space below.

1. Take three test tubes and label them A, B and C. Add 10 drops of the corresponding liquid to each test tube. Add a 1 cm depth of bromine water to each test tube and shake the mixture.

2. Take three test tubes and label them A, B and C. Add 10 drops of the corresponding liquid to each test tube. Add 1 cm³ acidified potassium dichromate to each test tube and warm the mixture in a 60 °C water bath for 5 minutes.

3. Take three test tubes and label them A, B and C. Add 10 drops of the corresponding liquid to each test tube. Add 1 cm³ of Fehling's solution to each test tube and warm the mixture in the water bath.

4. Take three test tubes and label them A, B and C. Add 10 drops of the corresponding liquid to each test tube. Add 1 cm³ of ethanol and 1 cm³ of dilute sodium hydroxide solution to each test tube, and warm the mixture in the water bath for five minutes. Acidify each mixture with dilute nitric acid and then add five drops of silver nitrate solution.

Results (Use this space to record your results for Part 1.)

Part 2

Perform the following tests on each of the inorganic solids X, Y and Z. Record your observations in the space on the following page.

1. Conduct flame tests for each of the three solids.

2. Take three test tubes and label them X, Y and Z. Add 10 cm³ distilled water to each test tube. Dissolve a spatula full of each solid in the corresponding test tube. Divide each solution into three portions.

   (a) To the first portion, add 5 cm³ dilute nitric acid followed by 10 drops of silver nitrate solution. Then add dilute ammonia solution.

   (b) To the second portion, add 5 cm³ dilute nitric acid followed by 10 drops of barium chloride solution.

   (c) To the third portion, add 2 cm³ of chlorine water.

Objectives

- To identify several unknown colourless liquids and inorganic solids

Equipment

- dropping bottle of A
- dropping bottle of B
- dropping bottle of C
- solid X
- solid Y
- solid Z
- bromine water
- spatula
- distilled water
- Fehling's solution
- 0.5 mol dm⁻³ barium chloride solution
- acidified potassium dichromate solution
- apparatus to conduct a flame test
- 0.1 mol dm⁻³ silver nitrate solution
- ethanol
- chlorine water
- dilute (1 mol dm⁻³) ammonia solution
- test tubes
- 250 ml beaker
- 1 mol dm⁻³ nitric acid
- dilute (1 mol dm⁻³) sodium hydroxide solution
- kettle

⚠ Safety

- Wear eye protection.
- Avoid skin contact with all the chemicals listed, including the 'unknowns'.
- Ammonia solution gives off ammonia gas, which must not be inhaled, especially by anyone with a respiratory problem.
- Ethanol is flammable.

Results (Use this space to record your results for Part 2.)

Learning tips

- Make sure you know the flame test colours for the ions of Group 1 and Group 2 elements.
- Negative test results are important as they tell you what your unknown substance is not.

Analysis of results

1   Which functional groups are in organic liquids A, B and C?

2   Identify the inorganic solids X, Y and Z.

Questions

An organic liquid product will form during some of the reactions in Part 1, tests 1–4. Identify these reactions and state the type of organic liquid product formed in each case.

....

....

....

....

....

....

....

....

Write ionic equations for the reactions of X, Y and Z in Part 2, test 2.

Why is nitric acid added in the test for halide ions using silver nitrate?

....

....

....

....

....

....

....

CORE PRACTICAL 9A:

FOLLOWING THE RATE OF THE IODINE–PROPANONE REACTION BY A TITRIMETRIC METHOD

Procedure

1 Mix 25 cm³ of 1 mol dm⁻³ aqueous propanone with 25 cm³ of 1 mol dm⁻³ sulfuric acid in a beaker.

2 Start the stop clock the moment you add 50 cm³ of 0.02 mol dm⁻³ iodine solution. Shake the beaker to mix well.

3 Using a pipette, withdraw a 10 cm³ sample of the mixture and transfer it to a conical flask.

4 Stop the reaction by adding a spatula measure of sodium hydrogencarbonate. Note the exact time at which the sodium hydrogencarbonate is added.

5 Titrate the remaining iodine present in the sample with 0.01 mol dm⁻³ sodium thiosulfate(VI) solution, using starch indicator. Record your results in the table below.

6 Repeat steps **3–5** at suitable time intervals (approximately every 3 minutes). Always note the exact time at which the sodium hydrogencarbonate is added.

Objectives

- To determine the rate of a reaction using a continuous monitoring method
- To determine the order of reaction with respect to a substance using a concentration–time graph

Equipment

- 50 cm³ of 1.0 mol dm⁻³ aqueous propanone solution
- 50 cm³ of 1.0 mol dm⁻³ sulfuric aci
- 50 cm³ of 0.02 mol dm⁻³ iodine solution (in 0.2 mol dm⁻³ potassium iodide solution)
- 0.01 mol dm⁻³ sodium thiosulfate(VI) solution
- 20 cm³ of 1% starch solution/indicator
- sodium hydrogencarbonate
- 100 cm³ beaker
- conical flasks
- 10 cm³ graduated pipette plus safety filler
- spatula
- stop clock

Results (Use this space to record your results.)

Time hydrogencarbonate added/min					
Initial reading/cm³					
Final reading/cm³					
Titre/cm³					

Learning tips

- The reaction between propanone and iodine in aqueous solution can be catalysed by an acid:

$$I_2(aq) + CH_3COCH_3(aq) + H^+(aq) \rightarrow CH_3COCH_2I(aq) + 2H^+(aq) + I^-(aq)$$

- You can study the influence of the iodine on the reaction rate if the concentrations of propanone and hydrogen ions effectively remain constant during the reaction. You can achieve this by using a large excess of both propanone and sulfuric acid in the starting reaction mixture.

⚠ Safety

- **WARNING!** The product from the reaction, iodopropanone, is a lachrymator (strongly irritant to the eyes). The reaction mixtu should be poured down a fume cupboard sink with plenty of running water immediately once each measurement is complete.

- Perform a risk assessment using up-to-date information before this practical is carried out.

- Wear eye protection.

- Sodium thiosulfate releases sulfur dioxide in this reaction, an propanone is flammable. Ensure that the room is well-ventilated.

- Avoid skin contact with the reactants and products.

- Do not run this practical for mo than 12 minutes in total.

Analysis of results

Plot a graph of titre against time. (The titre is proportional to the concentration of iodine.)

Use your graph to deduce the order of reaction with respect to iodine.

Questions

Similar experiments show that the reaction is first order with respect to propanone and to hydrogen ions. Use this information to answer the following questions.

1 What will be the effect on the rate if the concentration of the hydrogen ions is doubled?

....

....

2 What will be the effect on the rate if the concentration of the propanone is doubled?

....

....

3 What will be the effect on the rate if the concentration of the iodine is doubled?

....

....

4 Write the overall rate expression for this reaction.

5 Two students monitored the concentration of propanone as the reaction proceeded. They plotted a concentration–time graph from their results. What shape would you expect the graph to be? How would you use this graph to prove that the reaction is first order with respect to propanone?

....

....

....

....

....

....

....

....

....

....

....

Procedure

1. Measure 10.0 cm³ of potassium iodide solution into a small beaker standing on a white tile.
2. Add 5.0 cm³ of sodium thiosulfate solution to the potassium iodide solution.
3. Add 10 drops of starch solution to the mixture in the small beaker. Starch acts as the indicator and must be used in each experiment.
4. Measure out 10.0 cm³ of the sodium peroxodisulfate solution. Pour this into the mixture prepared in steps **1–3**. Start the stop clock.
5. Stop the clock when a blue colour appears in the beaker. Note the time taken.
6. Repeat steps **1–5** using the volumes of sodium peroxodisulfate solution and potassium iodide solution shown in Table 1. The total volume, including the sodium thiosulfate solution, must add up to 25.0 cm³; this can be achieved by adding the correct volume of distilled/deionised water.

Objectives

- To use a clock reaction to find the order of reaction with respect to iodide ions
- To use a clock reaction to find the order of reaction with respect to peroxodisulfate ions

Equipment

- 100 cm³ of 0.2 mol dm⁻³ sodium peroxodisulfate solution
- 100 cm³ of 0.2 mol dm⁻³ potassium iodide solution
- 50 cm³ of 0.05 mol dm⁻³ sodium thiosulfate solution
- 20 cm³ of 1% starch solution
- distilled/deionised water
- white tile
- four 10 cm³ measuring cylinders
- dropping pipettes
- nine 100 cm³ beakers
- stop clock

⚠ Safety

- Wear eye protection.
- Avoid skin contact with the reactants and products.

Table 1

Mixture	Volume $S_2O_8^{2-}$/cm³	Volume I^-/cm³	Volume $S_2O_3^{2-}$/cm³	Volume H_2O/cm³
A	10.0	10.0	5.0	0.0
B	10.0	8.0	5.0	2.0
C	10.0	6.0	5.0	4.0
D	10.0	4.0	5.0	6.0
E	10.0	2.0	5.0	8.0
F	8.0	10.0	5.0	2.0
G	6.0	10.0	5.0	4.0
H	4.0	10.0	5.0	6.0
I	2.0	10.0	5.0	8.0

Learning tips

The initial rate of a reaction is the instantaneous rate at the start of the reaction when the time, t, is zero ($t = 0$). You can find the initial rate by measuring the gradient of a tangent drawn at $t = 0$ on a concentration–time graph.

A clock reaction allows you to determine the initial rate of a reaction in a more convenient way, by taking a single measurement. The time, t, is measured from the start of an experiment until a visual change is observed. This often involves a colour change or the formation of a precipitate.

If there is no significant change in rate during this time, we can assume that the average rate of reaction will be the same as the initial rate.

The initial rate is then proportional to $\frac{1}{t}$.

Results (Use this space to record your results, in the form of a table with blank columns for the calculation of concentrations and rates.)

Analysis of results

In questions **1–4**, consider the first five solutions (**A–E**) in Table 1.

Calculate the concentration of iodide ions in each solution. Remember, the total volume of each solution is $25.0\,cm^3$. Write these values in a results table.

Use the times recorded to work out the rate of reaction for each solution. Write these values in your results table.

Plot a graph of rate against concentration.

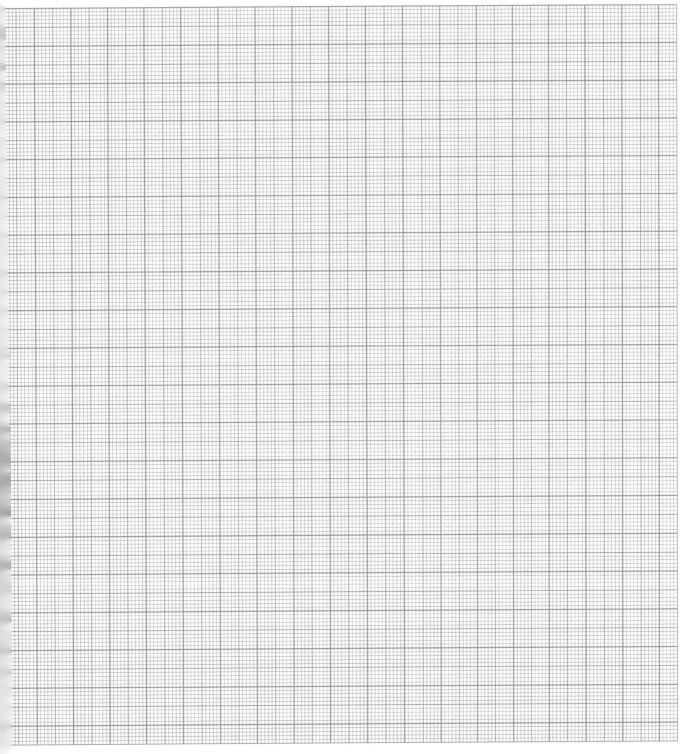

Use your graph to determine the order of the reaction with respect to iodide ions.

....

In questions **5–8**, consider solution **A** and solutions **F–I** from Table 1.

5 Work out the concentration of peroxodisulfate ions in 25.0 cm³ of each solution. Write these values in your results table.

6 Work out the rate of reaction for each solution. Write these values in your results table.

7 Plot a graph of rate against concentration.

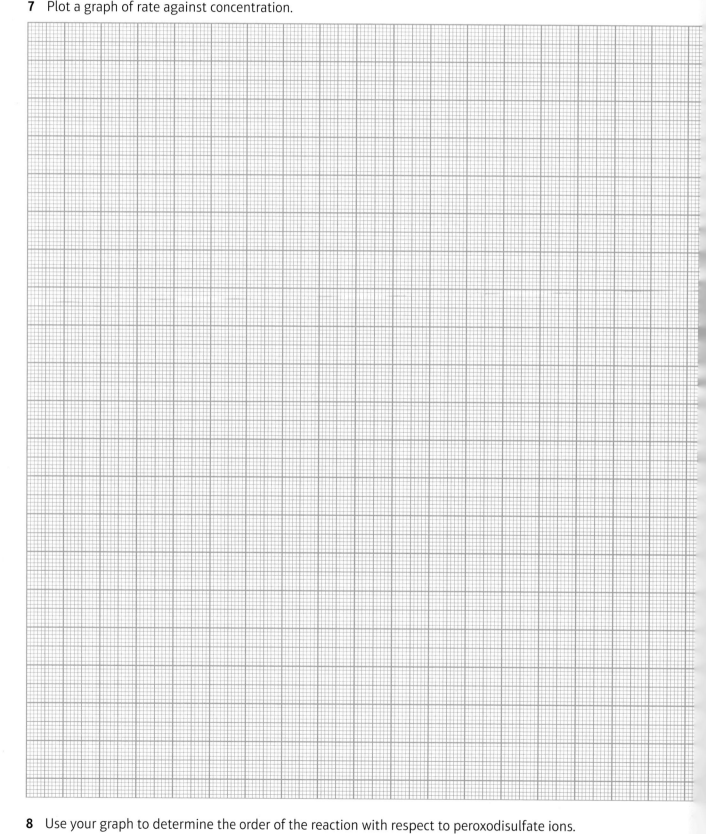

8 Use your graph to determine the order of the reaction with respect to peroxodisulfate ions.

....

Questions

1 Identify the main sources of uncertainty in the procedure used and the measurements recorded in this experiment. Calculate the percentage uncertainty for any measurements taken.

2 Suggest ways of minimising these uncertainties.

....

....

....

....

....

....

What is the overall rate equation for this reaction? The equation for the reaction is:

$$S_2O_8^{2-} + 2I^- \rightarrow 2SO_4^{2-} + I_2$$

A suggested mechanism for the reaction is:

step 1 $I^- + S_2O_8^{2-} \rightarrow (S_2O_8I)^{3-}$

step 2 $(S_2O_8I)^{3-} + I^- \rightarrow 2SO_4^{2-} + I_2$

Which of these steps is the rate-determining step? Use the rate equation to justify your answer.

....

....

....

....

Procedure

1 Pipette 10 cm³ of phenol solution and 10 cm³ of bromide/bromate solution into one boiling tube.

2 Add four drops of methyl red indicator to the mixture.

3 Pipette 5 cm³ of sulfuric acid solution into another boiling tube.

4 Use a kettle and a beaker to prepare a water bath with a temperature of 75 °C (±1 °C). Stand the two boiling tubes in the water bath.

5 When the contents of the boiling tubes have reached the temperature of the water bath, mix the contents of the two tubes by pouring rapidly from one tube into the other and then pouring the mixture back into the empty test tube. Start the stop clock at the same time.

6 Leave the boiling tube containing the reaction mixture in the water bath and time until the colour of the methyl red indicator disappears.

7 Record your results in the first two columns of the table below.

8 Repeat the whole experiment at 65 °C, 55 °C, 45 °C, 35 °C, 25 °C and 15 °C. Use ice to achieve the lowest temperature.

Results

1 Record your results in the table below.

2 Convert temperatures in °C to kelvin, K, and fill in the third column of the table. (0 °C = 273 K)

3 Calculate the reciprocal of each temperature (in K) and write the values in the fourth column of the table.

4 Take natural logs of the times and fill in the fifth column of the table.

Temp, T/°C	Time, t/s	T/K	$\frac{1}{T}$/K^{-1}	ln t

Objectives

- To use the Arrhenius equation to determine the activation energy of a reaction

Equipment

- 70 cm³ of 0.01 mol dm⁻³ aqueous phenol solution
- 70 cm³ bromide/bromate solution
- 50 cm³ of 0.5 mol dm⁻³ sulfuric acid
- methyl red indicator
- three 100 cm³ beakers
- four boiling tubes
- 10 cm³ pipette
- thermometer (0–110 °C)
- stop clock
- two 500 cm³ beakers
- kettle

⚠ Safety

- Wear eye protection and suitable chemical-resistant gloves.
- Avoid skin contact with the reactants and products.
- Do not inhale any fumes that may be produced.

Learning tips

- The Arrhenius equation is an exponential relationship between the rate constant, k, and the temperature, T.

$$k = Ae^{-\frac{E_a}{RT}}$$

where R = the gas constant = $8.314\,J\,mol^{-1}\,K^{-1}$, T = temperature in kelvin and E_a = activation energy of the reaction.

$k \propto$ reaction rate $\propto \dfrac{1}{t}$ so we can say that:

$$k = \frac{a\ constant,\ c}{time\ taken\ for\ methyl\ red\ to\ bleach} = \frac{c}{t}$$

- The Arrhenius equation can also be expressed as a logarithmic relationship:

$$\ln k = -\frac{E_a}{RT} + \ln A \quad \text{or} \quad \ln\left(\frac{c}{t}\right) = -\frac{E_a}{RT} + \ln A$$

Rearranging: $\ln t = \ln c - \ln A + \dfrac{E_a}{RT}$

Because $\ln c$ and $\ln A$ are constants, a graph of $\ln t$ against $\dfrac{1}{T}$ has a gradient of $\dfrac{E_a}{R}$.

Analysis of results

Plot a graph of your results on the following page.

2 Find the gradient of your graph.

Use your answer to question **2** to calculate the activation energy of the reaction, E_a.

Plot a graph of $\ln t$ (on the y-axis) against $\frac{1}{T}$ (on the x-axis).

Questions

Write an equation for the reaction between bromine and phenol.

What is the function of the methyl red in this experiment?

....

....

....

....

....

....

CORE PRACTICAL 11:

FINDING THE K_a VALUE FOR A WEAK ACID

Procedure

1   Set up the datalogger to read the pH, or calibrate the pH meter.

2   Pipette 25.0 cm³ of 0.1 mol dm⁻³ ethanoic acid solution into a 250 cm³ conical flask.

3   Fill a burette with sodium hydroxide solution.

4   Add two or three drops of phenolphthalein to the conical flask.

5   Titrate the ethanoic acid solution with sodium hydroxide solution until the mixture *just* turns pink. Swirl the mixture to ensure the end point has been reached.

6   Pipette a further 25.0 cm³ of 0.1 mol dm⁻³ ethanoic acid solution into the 250 cm³ conical flask.

7   Record the pH of this solution.

Results (Use this space to record your results.)

Objectives

● To determine K_a for a weak acid

Equipment

● 100 cm³ of 0.1 mol dm⁻³ ethanoic acid solution

● 100 cm³ of 0.1 mol dm⁻³ sodium hydroxide solution

● datalogger and pH probe or pH meter

● stand, clamp and boss for pH probe

● 50 cm³ burette

● burette stand

● 250 cm³ conical flask

● 25 cm³ pipette and filler

● phenolphthalein indicator

⚠ Safety

● Wear eye protection.

● Avoid skin contact with the reactants and products.

● Take care when clamping and filling the burette that it does not crack or topple over.

.earning tips

The ionisation of an acid is shown by:

$$HA(aq) \rightleftharpoons H^+(aq) + A^-(aq)$$

Because an equilibrium is set up, an equilibrium constant, K_a, can be written:

$$K_a = \frac{[H^+][A^-]}{[HA]}$$

- The K_a value is an indication of acid strength. The larger the value of the K_a, the stronger the acid.
- You can measure the K_a of a weak acid by titrating a known volume of the acid against sodium hydroxide, using phenolphthalein as an indicator. Then add a further equal volume of acid, and measure the pH of the resulting solution. Because effectively half of the acid has been titrated:

$$[HA] = [A^-]$$

$[A^-]$ and $[HA]$ can be cancelled in $K_a = \frac{[H^+][A^-]}{[HA]}$

Therefore $K_a = [H^+]$

- The pH value of the combined solutions can be converted to $[H^+]$ to give a K_a value.

.nalysis of results

ecord the pH of the solution after the second addition of ethanoic acid.

ow work through the following questions to calculate the K_a value for ethanoic acid.

uestions

Use the pH of your solution to calculate $[H^+]$.

Calculate a value of K_a for ethanoic acid.

3 Identify some of the sources of uncertainty in this experiment.
   What can you do to overcome them?

....

....

....

....

....

....

....

....

....

....

....

....

....

Procedure

1. Use sandpaper to clean the strips of zinc and copper.

2. Set up a zinc half-cell by pouring 50 cm³ of zinc sulfate solution into the 100 cm³ beaker and standing the strip of zinc in the beaker.

3. Set up a copper half-cell by pouring 50 cm³ of copper(II) sulfate solution into a separate 100 cm³ beaker and standing the strip of copper in the beaker.

4. Make an electrical connection between the two beakers by joining them with a strip of filter paper that has been dipped in a saturated solution of potassium nitrate (this acts as a salt bridge).

5. Use the connecting wires and crocodile clips to join the two metal strips with a voltmeter.

6. Record the electrode potential of the [Zn(s) | Zn²⁺(aq)] and [Cu²⁺(aq) | Cu(s)] system. If the voltmeter gives a negative value, reverse the connections so that it gives a positive value.

7. Repeat steps **1–6** using the following combinations of metal/metal ion half-cells. Remember to clean the metal strips with sandpaper before use.

   [Zn(s) | Zn²⁺(aq)] and [Fe²⁺(aq) | Fe(s)]

   [Fe(s) | Fe²⁺(aq)] and [Cu²⁺(aq) | Cu(s)]

   [Zn(s) | Zn²⁺(aq)] and [Ag⁺(aq) | Ag(s)]

   [Cu(s) | Cu²⁺(aq)] and [Ag⁺(aq) | Ag(s)]

Results (Use this space to record your results.)

Learning tips

- To calculate electrode potentials, use the equation:

  $E_{cell} = E_{\text{right-hand half-cell}} - E_{\text{left-hand half-cell}}$

- Note that the concentration of silver nitrate is $0.1\,mol\,dm^{-3}$, which is less than that of the other solutions. It would be particularly dangerous to handle $1.0\,mol\,dm^{-3}$ silver nitrate.

Analysis of results

1 In one of the cells you set up, the [Fe(s) | Fe^{2+}(aq)] and [Cu^{2+}(aq) | Cu(s)] system:

   $E^{\ominus}$ [Fe^{2+}(aq) | Fe(s)] = $-0.44\,V$

Use these values to calculate $E[Cu^{2+}$(aq) | Cu(s)] for your half-cell.

2 Calculate $E[Zn^{2+}$(aq) | Zn(s)] for your half-cell.

Questions

1 The electrode potential values for the cells you set up may be slightly different to theoretical values for standard electrode potentials. Give a reason for this.

....

....

....

....

....

2 Give a reason it would be dangerous to use a 1.0 mol dm^{-3} solution of silver nitrate.

....

....

....

....

[Mg^{2+}(aq) | Mg(s)] can also be used as a half-cell. Describe a problem that might be observed with this system.

....

....

....

....

....

....

Procedure

1 Crush the iron tablets using the pestle and mortar.

2 Transfer the crushed tablets to a weighing boat and measure the combined mass of the tablets and weighing boat. Record this mass.

3 Empty the crushed tablets into the small beaker and reweigh the weighing boat. Record this mass.

4 Add most of the $100\,cm^3$ of $1.5\,mol\,dm^{-3}$ sulfuric acid to the small beaker. Stir to dissolve as much of the tablets as possible.

5 Filter the solution (to remove any undissolved solids) into the volumetric flask. Rinse the beaker with the rest of the sulfuric acid and filter the washings into the volumetric flask. Add distilled/deionised water to make up the solution to the mark. Stopper and shake.

6 Pipette $25.0\,cm^3$ of this solution into the conical flask.

7 Titrate the iron(II) solution with potassium manganate(VII) solution until the mixture has *just* turned pink. On standing, the pink colour will disappear because there is a secondary reaction between the $KMnO_4$ and another ingredient in the tablet. *Do not add any more $KMnO_4$.*

8 Record your results in the table below.

9 Repeat the titration until you obtain concordant results.

10 Have one of your burette readings checked by your teacher or a technician.

Results (Use this space to record your results.)

	Rough	1	2	3	4
Initial reading/cm³					
Final reading/cm³					
Titre/cm³					
Concordant (Y/N)					

Learning tips

● You need two equations:

$$\text{number of moles} = \text{concentration} \times \frac{\text{volume}}{1000}$$

$$\text{number of moles} = \frac{\text{mass}}{M_r}$$

When carrying out titration calculations, show all your working clearly and explain what you are doing in each step. If you do this, you will be able to gain marks in an exam even if you get the final answer wrong.

Analysis of results

Use concordant results to calculate the average titre.

Now answer the questions below to calculate the mass of iron in the tablet.

Questions

Combine the two half-equations given below to write the equation for the reaction between iron(II) ions and potassium manganate(VII):

$$Fe^{2+}(aq) \rightarrow Fe^{3+} + e^-$$
$$MnO_4^-(aq) + 8H^+(aq) + 5e^- \rightarrow Mn^{2+}(aq) + 4H_2O(l)$$

Use your average titre to calculate the number of moles of manganate(VII) ions used in the titration.

Use the equation to calculate the number of moles of iron(II) ions in the $25\,cm^3$ sample of iron(II) sulfate from the iron tablet.

4 Calculate the number of moles of iron(II) ions in the 250 cm³ volumetric flask at the start of the experiment.

5 Calculate the mass of iron in the original five iron tablets, and hence the mass of iron in one iron tablet. (M_r Fe = 55.8 g mol⁻¹)

6 Compare your value for the mass of iron in one tablet with the information from the supplier about the composition of each iron tablet. Suggest reasons for any difference between the two values.

7 Make a list of any procedural errors. Suggest ways in which these errors can be reduced.

8 Calculate the percentage measurement uncertainty for the burette.

Procedure

1. Wash the pipette, burette and conical flask with distilled water. The pipette should then be rinsed with potassium iodate(V) solution and the burette with sodium thiosulfate solution before the titration.

2. Using a pipette and filler, place 25 cm³ of potassium iodate solution into a conical flask. To this add 20 cm³ of dilute sulfuric acid and 10 cm³ of potassium iodide solution.

3. Fill the burette with sodium thiosulfate solution using a funnel.

4. Place the conical flask on the white tile and titrate the prepared mixture against the sodium thiosulfate. The initial colour of the mixture is yellow and the endpoint of the titration is colourless. Keep adding sodium thiosulfate while swirling until the solution turns a pale yellow colour. At this point add 5 drops of starch solution. The resulting mixture will turn blue-black.

5. Continue the titration, but add the sodium thiosulfate drop by drop with thorough swirling. The end-point of the titration is detected by a colour change from blue-black to colourless.

6. Write down the burette reading. Repeat the titration until you obtain concordant results. Have one of your burette readings checked by your teacher or a technician.

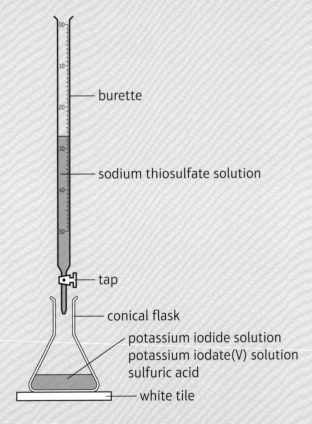

burette

sodium thiosulfate solution

tap

conical flask

potassium iodide solution
potassium iodate(V) solution
sulfuric acid

white tile

Objectives

- To calculate the concentration of an oxidising agent, potassium iodate(V) (KIO₃)

Equipment

- potassium iodate(V) solution
- 0.05 mol dm⁻³ potassium iodide solution
- 1.0 mol dm⁻³ sulfuric acid
- 0.1 mol dm⁻³ sodium thiosulfate solution
- distilled water
- pipette and filler
- burette
- filter funnel
- white tile
- conical flask
- starch solution in dropping bottle
- clamp and stand

⚠ Safety

- Wear goggles.
- Avoid skin contact with the reactants and products.
- Take care when clamping and filling the burette that it does not crack or topple over.

Learning tip

You need this equation for titration calculations:

$$\text{number of moles} = \text{concentration} \times \frac{\text{volume}}{1000}$$

Results (Use this space to record your results.)

	Rough	1	2	3	4
Initial reading/cm³					
Final reading/cm³					
Titre/cm³					
Concordant (Y/N)					

Analysis of results

1   Use concordant results to calculate the average titre.

Now answer the questions below to calculate the concentration of the potassium iodate(V) solution.

Questions

1   Write a balanced ionic equation to show what is happening in the conical flask after the starting reagents are added but before the titration.

2   Why is this initial reaction carried out?

....

....

Write a balanced ionic equation to represent the titration.

Why is sodium thiosulfate used in the titration?

Why is starch solution used?

Why is starch solution not added at the start of the titration?

Calculate how many moles of I_2 have been made in the first reaction.
(**Hint**: Have a look back to the Learning Tips section and the equation you wrote in Question 3.)

Calculate the concentration of potassium iodate(V).
(**Hint**: You will need to use the equation from Question 1 – make sure you have balanced it properly!)

Why is the conical flask *not* rinsed with the solution it is to contain?

Procedure

1. Weigh between 1.4 g and 1.6 g of copper(II) sulfate. To do this, you should weigh a test tube and record its mass. Then add the copper(II) sulfate to the test tube, reweigh and record the mass. The mass of the copper(II) sulfate is the difference between the two masses.

2. Add 4 cm³ of water to the test tube using a graduated pipette.

3. Prepare a water bath by pouring hot water from a kettle into a 100 cm³ beaker. Stand the test tube in the water bath. Stir gently to dissolve the copper(II) sulfate.

4. Pipette 6 cm³ of ethanol into a beaker.

5. Remove the test tube containing the copper(II) sulfate solution from the water bath.

6. Perform this step in the fume cupboard, wearing gloves. Stirring all the time, add 2 cm³ of concentrated ammonia solution to the copper(II) sulfate solution.

7. Pour the contents of the test tube into the beaker containing the ethanol. Mix well and then cool the mixture in an ice bath.

8. Using a Büchner funnel and flask, filter the crystals. Wash your test tube with cold ethanol and add the washings to the Büchner funnel. Finally, rinse the crystals with cold ethanol.

9. Carefully scrape the crystals off the filter paper onto a fresh piece of filter paper. Cover the crystals with a second piece of filter paper. Carefully pat the paper to dry the crystals. Note: to get the crystals completely dry, you may need to move them to dry parts of the filter paper several times.

10. Once the crystals are dry, measure and record their mass.

Results (Use this space to record your results.)

Objectives

- To prepare a transition metal complex, tetraamminecopper(II) sulfate-1-water

Equipment

- copper(II) sulfate pentahydrate ($CuSO_4 \cdot 5H_2O$)
- 10 cm³ ethanol
- 2 cm³ concentrated ammonia solution
- crushed ice
- Büchner flask and funnel and vacuum filtration apparatus
- filter paper
- one test tube
- one 50 cm³ beaker
- one 100 cm³ beaker
- one 10 cm³ graduated pipette
- one pipette filler
- one spatula
- one stirring rod
- mass balance (2 d.p.) and weighing boat
- access to a kettle

⚠ Safety

- Wear eye protection.
- The ammonia solution should only be used in a working fume cupboard while wearing suitable chemical resistant gloves.
- The water bath must not be heated with a Bunsen burner as ethanol is highly flammable

Learning tip

• Do not discard any solutions during the filtering and washing process until you are confident that you have the final product.

Analysis of results

1 Record the mass of copper(II) sulfate used in the reaction.

2 Record the yield of dry tetraamminecopper(II) sulfate-1-water obtained.

Questions

Write the equation for this reaction.

Calculate the relative formula masses of $CuSO_4 \cdot 5H_2O$ and $Cu(NH_3)_4SO_4 \cdot H_2O$.

Calculate the number of moles of copper(II) sulfate used in the reaction.

Use your answer to question **3** to calculate the theoretical yield of tetraamminecopper(II) sulfate-1-water that your reaction should have produced.

5 Calculate the percentage yield obtained in this reaction.

6 Comment on your percentage yield. Explain any loss or gain in mass compared with the theoretical yield.

Part A: Identifying inorganic ions

1 Conduct some research to find out how to carry out a flame test to identify metal cations. Make sure you cite any sources using an appropriate format.

2 Write a plan for the safe conduct of a flame-test experiment. Describe in detail how you would carry out the experiment and the results you would expect.

3 Conduct some research to find out how to use sodium hydroxide to identify metal cations. Make sure you cite any sources using an appropriate format.

4 Write a plan for the safe conduct of this experiment. Describe in detail how you would carry out the experiment and the results you would expect.

Objectives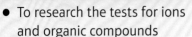

- To research the tests for ions and organic compounds
- To successfully test unknown substances to establish their identity

Equipment

- concentrated hydrochloric acid
- $1\,mol\,dm^{-3}$ sodium hydroxide
- $1\,mol\,dm^{-3}$ nitric acid
- $0.1\,mol\,dm^{-3}$ silver nitrate solution
- $1\,mol\,dm^{-3}$ ammonia solution
- $1\,mol\,dm^{-3}$ dilute hydrochloric acid
- barium chloride solution
- limewater
- bromine water
- sodium carbonate solution
- ethanol
- concentrated sulfuric acid
- four tubs labelled A, B, C and D
- three bottles labelled X, Y and Z
- nichrome wire
- delivery tube
- Bunsen burner and safety mat
- test tubes and bungs
- distilled water
- dropping pipette
- spatula
- boiling tube
- $250\,cm^3$ beaker
- $100\,cm^3$ beaker
- kettle

⚠ Safety

- Wear eye protection.
- Beware of 'spitting' – hot particles flying off the flame test wire when it is in the flame.
- Do not open or dispense (pour) flammable liquids anywhere near a flame.
- Avoid skin contact with the reactants and products.

5 Conduct some research to find out how to use silver nitrate to identify halide ions. Make sure you cite any sources using an appropriate format.

6 Write a plan for the safe conduct of this experiment. Describe in detail how you would carry out the experiment and the results you would expect.

7 Conduct some research to find out how to test for sulfate ions. Make sure you cite any sources using an appropriate format.

8 Write a plan for the safe conduct of this experiment. Describe in detail how you would carry out the experiment and the results you would expect.

9 Conduct some research to find out how to test for carbonate ions. Make sure you cite any sources using an appropriate format.

10 Write a plan for the safe conduct of this experiment. Describe in detail how you would carry out the experiment and the results you would expect.

11 Carry out your experiments to identify substances A–D. Pay particular attention to the management of safety.

Results (Use this space to record your results for the experiments in Part A. Use these results to identify substances A–D.)

Part B: Analysis of organic compounds

1   Conduct some research to find out how to test for alkenes. Make sure you cite any sources using an appropriate format.

2   Write a plan for the safe conduct of an experiment to test for alkenes. Describe in detail how you would carry out the experiment and the results you would expect.

3   Conduct some research to find out how to test for an aldehyde. Make sure you cite any sources using an appropriate format.

4   Write a plan for the safe conduct of an experiment to test for aldehydes. Describe in detail how you would carry out the experiment and the results you would expect.

5   Conduct some research to find out how to test for carboxylic acids. Make sure you cite any sources using an appropriate format.

6   Write a plan for the safe conduct of an experiment to test for carboxylic acids. Describe in detail how you would carry out the experiment and the results you would expect.

Carry out your experiments to identify substances X–Z. Take appropriate safety precautions.

Results (Use this space to record your results for the experiments in Part B. Use these results to identify substances X–Z.)

Questions

1 When you are testing an inorganic compound for the presence of halide ions, why is nitric acid added before you add silver nitrate?

....

....

....

....

....

....

2 What further test could you carry out to distinguish between sulfate(VI) ions and sulfate(IV) ions?

....

....

....

....

....

....

3 Outline a further test you could use to identify the presence of an aldehyde group.

....

....

....

....

....

....

Procedure

Weigh 2 g of 2-hydroxybenzoic acid and put it in a pear-shaped flask. Clamp the flask and suspend it in a beaker of water.

Add 5 cm³ of ethanoic anhydride to the 2-hydroxybenzoic acid. Add five drops of concentrated sulfuric acid to the mixture in the flask. Fix a condenser on the flask.

In a well-ventilated room, use a Bunsen burner to carefully warm the mixture in the water bath. Gently swirl the mixture until all the solid has dissolved.

Continue warming the mixture for another 10 minutes.

Remove the flask from the hot water bath. Add 10 cm³ of crushed ice and some distilled/deionised water to the reaction mixture to break down any unreacted ethanoic anhydride.

Stand the flask in a beaker of iced water until precipitation appears to be complete.

Filter off the product using a Büchner funnel and suction apparatus.

Wash the crystals with the minimum volume of iced water.

Recrystallise the aspirin in the minimum volume of a mixture of ethanol and water (1:3).

0 Filter and dry the crystals.

1 Measure the mass of the pure, dry crystals.

2 Measure the melting point of the product using melting point apparatus.

Results (Use this space to record your results.)

Objectives

- To perform and explain the reactions of acid anhydrides
- To synthesise aspirin from 2-hydroxybenzoic acid

Equipment

- 10 cm³ ethanoic anhydride
- 2 g 2-hydroxybenzoic acid
- 1 cm³ concentrated sulfuric acid
- distilled/deionised water
- ethanol
- two 10 cm³ measuring cylinders
- condenser
- small pear-shaped flask
- stand, clamp and boss
- two 250 cm³ beakers
- dropping pipette
- ice
- Bunsen burner, tripod, gauze and safety mat
- mass balance (2 d.p.) and weighing boat
- Büchner funnel, Büchner flask, water/suction pump and filter paper to fit funnel
- melting point apparatus and melting point tube

⚠ Safety

- Wear eye protection.
- A working fume cupboard should be used if the room cannot be well ventilated, for example, because the group size is too large.
- Ethanol is flammable.
- Avoid skin contact with the reactants and products.

Learning tip

$$\text{Percentage yield} = \frac{\text{actual yield}}{\text{expected yield}} \times 100$$

Analysis of results and questions

1 Which functional group of the 2-hydroxybenzoic acid reacts with the ethanoic anhydride?

....

2 Draw the structural formulae for the reactants and product involved in the formation of aspirin from 2-hydroxybenzoic acid.

3 Calculate the relative molecular masses of 2-hydroxybenzoic acid and aspirin.

Calculate the theoretical yield.

Calculate the percentage yield.

Why might the apparent yield be higher than the theoretical yield?

....

....

....

What would you expect to be the main impurity in your sample?

....

....

The actual melting temperature of aspirin is 136 °C. Is this similar to the value you recorded?
Why do you think there might have been a difference?

....

....

....

....

....

....

ANSWERS

Core Practical 1

1 $CaCO_3 + 2CH_3COOH \rightarrow Ca(CH_3COO)_2 + CO_2 + H_2O$

2 This method allows for the mass of any calcium carbonate that remains in the test tube after it has been tipped out.

3 Some gas is lost before the bung is replaced in the boiling tube.

4 Place a tube containing the acid inside the vessel containing the calcium carbonate, then tip to mix the reagent (so the vessel remains closed at all times).

5 When 0.40 g of calcium carbonate is used:

moles $CaCO_3 = \dfrac{0.4}{100.1} = 0.003996$

moles ethanoic acid $= c \times v = 1 \times \dfrac{30}{1000} = 0.03$

moles acid is more than 2 × moles calcium carbonate – so ethanoic acid is in excess

Core Practical 2

1 Heat energy must be supplied; hence, the temperature change measured is not solely due to the decomposition.

2 moles hydrochloric acid = 2 × 30
1000 = 0.06 mol
mol K_2CO_3 = 3
138.2 = 0.022 mol
This reacts with 0.0434 moles of hydrochloric acid.
mol $KHCO_3$ = 3.5
100.1 = 0.035 mol
This reacts with 0.035 moles of hydrochloric acid.
Moles hydrochloric acid (0.06) is more than 2 × moles potassium carbonate and more than 1 × moles potassium hydrogencarbonate – so hydrochloric acid is in excess in both reactions.

3 Reaction 1 – diagram shows exothermic reaction

Reaction 2 – diagram shows endothermic reaction

Reaction 3 – diagram shows endothermic reaction

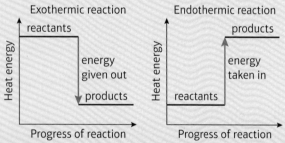

4 Polystyrene is a better insulator than glass. Therefore, less heat energy is lost to/gained from the surroundings, and the measured temperature changes are more accurate.

Core Practical 3

1 $HCl + NaOH \rightarrow NaCl + H_2O$

2 a $2NaOH + CO_2 \rightarrow Na_2CO_3 + H_2O$

    b   i   The concentration will decrease.

       ii   The volume of sodium hydroxide solution required will not change because the sodium carbonate produced will also react with the hydrochloric acid. Two moles of sodium carbonate react to make one mole of sodium hydroxide which will react with two moles of hydrochloric acid; this is the same number of moles of hydrochloric acid that the sodium hydroxide would have reacted with.

3 The percentage error will be greater for smaller titres than for larger titres.

Core Practical 4

1 $\dfrac{0.6}{250} \times 100 = 0.24\%$

2 $\dfrac{0.05 \times 2}{\text{titre selected}} \times 100$

3 Any water left in the pipette will dilute the sodium hydroxide solution, changing the number of moles used.

4 Water in the conical flask will not change the number of moles of sodium hydroxide – the volume of sodium hydroxide is measured before it is put into the flask.

5 Phenolphthalein; changes from pink to colourless.

Core Practical 5

1 $CH_3CH_2CH_2CH_2Br + H_2O \rightarrow CH_3CH_2CH_2CH_2OH + H^+ + Br^-$

2 Silver iodide.

3 The halogenoalkanes are insoluble in water. Using ethanol ensures that the halogenoalkanes dissolve so they can react with the water molecules.

4 Water has lone pair(s) of electrons on the oxygen atom.

5 If hydroxide ions were used, a precipitate of silver hydroxide would form instantly.

6

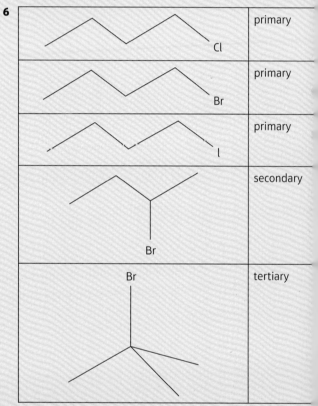

Core Practical 6

1 $(CH_3)_3COH + HCl \rightarrow (CH_3)_3CCl + H_2O$

2 (unreacted) HCl

$HCl + NaHCO_3 \rightarrow NaCl + CO_2 + H_2O$

3 2-methylpropan-2-ol can form hydrogen bonds, 2-chloro-2-methylpropane cannot.

2-methylpropan-2-ol is able to form hydrogen bonds with wa and so it is soluble in water.

2-chloro-2-methylpropane cannot form hydrogen bonds with water and so it is insoluble in water.

Intermolecular hydrogen bonds in 2-methylpropan-2-ol are stronger than the dipole-dipole attractions and London force between molecules in 2-chloro-2-methylpropane, so more energy is required to separate the molecules.

Core Practical 7

1 Heating under reflux involves boiling a reaction mixture, cool the vapours in a condenser and returning them to the mixtur It is a simple and effective way of maintaining a constant reaction temperature. As organic reactions can be very slow, ensures that the reaction takes place without the reaction fla boiling dry.

2 Adding propan-1-ol solution slowly prevents any dangerous splashing as the reaction is exothermic.

3 Anti-bumping granules are added to promote smooth, even boiling. The granules help prevent large bubbles forming in the reaction mixture when it is heated.

4 Feeding water in from the bottom of the condenser ensures that the entire condenser is filled with water. This produces efficient cooling.

5 Propanal has a low boiling point, so collecting the distillate at a low temperature prevents it immediately evaporating.

6 $CH_3CH_2CH_2OH + [O] \rightarrow CH_3CH_2CHO + H_2O$

7 $CH_3CH_2CH_2OH + 2[O] \rightarrow CH_3CH_2COOH + H_2O$

8

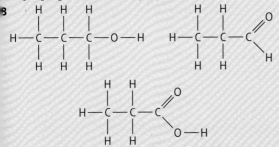

9 Heating the mixture under reflux means that the propanal produced is constantly returned to the reaction vessel, so it is further oxidised to propanoic acid.

10 Secondary alcohols are oxidised to ketones. For example, if propan-2-ol (a secondary alcohol) is heated with acidified potassium dichromate(VI) solution, propanone is formed.

Unlike in the oxidation of a primary alcohol, there is no lone hydrogen bonded to the carbon atom which has a double-bonded oxygen (the aldehyde group). So, it is not possible for any further oxygen to be added to produce a carboxylic acid.

Tertiary alcohols are not easily oxidised because, unlike primary and secondary alcohols, they do not have a hydrogen atom attached to the same carbon atom as the hydroxyl (OH) group.

re Practical 8

Test 1   B produces a 1,2-dibromo compound

Test 2   A produces a ketone/aldehyde/carboxylic acid

Test 3   No reactions

Test 4   C produces a bromoalkane

a $CO_3^{2-} + 2H^+ \rightarrow CO_2 + H_2O$
$Ag^+ + Br^- \rightarrow AgBr$

b $Ba^{2+} + SO_4^{2-} \rightarrow BaSO_4$

c $2Br^- + Cl_2 \rightarrow Br_2 + 2Cl^-$

To destroy/react with any carbonate ions so that a precipitate of silver carbonate does not form.

re Practical 9a

The rate will double.

The rate will double.

The rate will remain the same.

Rate = $k[H^+][CH_3COCH_3]$

The graph would be a curve. To prove that the reaction is first order, you can look at the half-life at various points; the half-life will be constant for a first-order reaction. Alternatively, plot a graph of rate against concentration; for a first-order reaction this will be a straight-line graph.

Core Practical 9b

1 One procedural error is misjudging the appearance of the blue colour in the solution.

Another arises from the addition of the starch, which increases the total volume of the mixture slightly.

Measurement uncertainties can occur when measuring volumes of solutions.

For a 2 cm³ volume, the uncertainty is ±0.1 cm³

% uncertainty = $\frac{0.2}{2} \times 100 = 10\%$

For a 10 cm³ volume, the uncertainty is ±0.1 cm³

% uncertainty = $\frac{0.2}{10} \times 100 = 2\%$

2 The procedural errors are difficult to overcome. One possible change is to have two students timing simultaneously and to use the average value.

Measurement uncertainties can be minimised by using a graduated pipette or a burette.

3 Rate = $k[S_2O_8^{2-}][I^-]$

4 Step 1 is the rate-determining step. The rate of the reaction is second order and involves one peroxodisulfate ion and one iodide ion.

Core Practical 10

1 $C_6H_5OH + 3Br_2 \rightarrow C_6H_2Br_3OH + 3HBr$

2 When all the phenol has reacted, the bromine continuously produced in the first reaction will react with the methyl red indicator, bleaching its colour. Thus, the methyl red acts as an indicator, showing when the reaction is complete.

Core Practical 11

1 This will depend on your findings but the pH should be 4.77; so [H⁺] = 1.7 × 10⁻⁵ mol dm⁻³.

2 1.7 × 10⁻⁵ mol dm⁻³

3 Sources of uncertainty include inaccuracy of burette readings, and difficulty identifying the exact end point. Read glassware from the bottom of the meniscus; use a white tile so you can see the colour change clearly.

Core Practical 12

1 The experiment was not carried out under standard conditions.

2 Silver nitrate is highly oxidising. An alternative answer is that silver nitrate is very expensive.

3 Magnesium reacts slowly with the water in the solution, raising the concentration of magnesium ions. The equilibrium will move to oppose this change and form more magnesium atoms.

Core Practical 13a

1 $5Fe^{2+} + MnO_4^- + 8H^+ \rightarrow 5Fe^{3+} + Mn^{2+} + 4H_2O$

2 If average titre = 21.40 cm³:

moles = concentration × $\frac{\text{volume}}{1000}$

moles = 0.005 × $\frac{21.40}{1000}$ = 0.000 107

moles of MnO_4^- = 0.000 107 moles

3 Moles of iron = 0.000 535 mol

4 Moles of iron in the 250 cm³ volumetric flask = 0.005 35 mol

5 0.005 35 moles = 0.3 g or 300 mg in five tablets or 60 mg in one tablet

6 The answer to this question will depend on your results but generally, the published result for an iron tablet is 65 mg of iron per tablet. There are a number of possible reasons for differences between the value you obtained and the value stated on the packaging, e.g.: The level of equipment and experience of the lab carrying out the tests for the manufacturer will be different and so produce different results. The results selected will be the best ones found in the research as they are trying to promote the product. The tests will be run on many more tablets than can be attempted in a school science lab and so will be a closer match to the average composition of a tablet.

ANSWERS

7 Procedural errors:
- Stirring may not be sufficient to ensure that all the iron dissolves – warming the solution may help.
- Transfer of the solution and filtering – ensure that the beaker and the filter paper are rinsed with water.
- The solution may not be mixed – invert the volumetric flask several times to ensure thorough mixing.
- Glassware measurements may not be read accurately – read glassware marks from the bottom of the meniscus.
- The end point may not be clear – use a white tile so you can see the end point clearly.

8 $\frac{0.05}{21.40} \times 100 = 0.23\%$

Core Practical 13b

1 $IO_3^- + 5I^- + 6H^+ \rightarrow 3I_2 + 3H_2O$

2 This reaction is carried out so that all the potassium iodate is used up in oxidising some of the I^- ions to I_2.

3 $I_2 + 2S_2O_3^{2-} \rightarrow 2I^- + S_4O_6^{2-}$

4 Sodium thiosulfate is used in the titration as it will react with the I_2 producing I^-. This will cause the colour of the reaction mixture to change from yellow to colourless.

5 The colour change from pale yellow to colourless is very difficult to see. The starch helps to make the end point visible as it produces a vivid colour change of blue-black to colourless.

6 Starch solution is not added at the start as it forms an insoluble complex with iodine.

7 The results might vary depending on the concentrations used. But If the average titre was 13.60 cm³ and the concentration of sodium thiosulfate was 0.1 mol dm⁻³, then:

number of moles = concentration × $\frac{\text{volume}}{1000}$

number of moles thiosulfate = $0.1 \times \frac{13.6}{1000}$ = 0.00136 mol

From the balanced ionic equation, we can see that the ratio of moles of iodine to thiosulfate is 1:2. This means that the number of moles of iodine is 0.00136 ÷ 2 = 0.00068 mol

8 From the first equation worked out in Question 1 (IO_3^- + $5I^-$ + $6H^+ \rightarrow 3I_2 + 3H_2O$), the ratio of iodine to iodate is 3:1.

number of moles of potassium iodate(V) = 0.00068 ÷ 3

number of moles of potassium iodate(V) = 0.00022667 mol

concentration = $\frac{\text{number of moles}}{\text{volume in dm}^3}$

concentration of potassium iodate(V) = $\frac{0.00022667}{[25 \div 1000]}$

concentration of potassium iodate(V) = 0.00906667 mol dm⁻³

9 If the conical flask was rinsed out with the solution it was to contain, then traces of the solution would remain. This would mean that you would not know precisely the amount of the solution in the flask.

Core Practical 14

1 $CuSO_4 \cdot 5H_2O + 4NH_3 \rightarrow Cu(NH_3)_4SO_4 \cdot H_2O + 4H_2O$

2 $CuSO_4 \cdot 5H_2O = 249.5$
$Cu(NH_3)_4SO_4 \cdot H_2O = 245.5$

3 0.006 01 moles (based on 1.5 g of $CuSO_4 \cdot 5H_2O$)

4 Theoretical yield of $Cu(NH_3)_4SO_4 \cdot H_2O$ (M_r 244.5) = 0.006 01 mol
$0.006\,01 \times 244.5\,g$ = 1.47 g

5 If 1.2 g were produced, percentage yield = $\frac{1.2}{1.48} \times 100 = 81\%$

6 Answers will depend on the percentage yield obtained. Losses could be due to the reaction not going to completion, so some product stays in solution rather than crystallising out. Gains could be due to crystals not being dry or not being pure.

Core Practical 15

1 The nitric acid removes anions – such as carbonate ions – that would form a precipitate with silver nitrate.

2 Add dilute hydrochloric acid; sulfate(IV) ions will dissolve but sulfate(VI) ions will not.

3 Heat with Fehling's or Benedict's solution; the formation of a precipitate indicates the presence of an aldehyde group.

Core Practical 16

1 The hydroxyl group

2

2-hydroxybenzoic acid + ethanoic anhydride → aspirin

3 2-hydroxybenzoic acid = 138; aspirin = 180

4 Theoretical yield: 1 mol 2-hydroxybenzoic acid gives 1 mol aspirin
2.00 g 2-hydroxybenzoic acid = $\frac{2.00}{138}$ mol gives $\frac{2.00}{138}$ mol aspirin
(M_r 180) = $\frac{2.00}{138} \times 180 = 2.6\,g$

5 This will depend on your results: $\frac{\text{actual yield}}{2.6} \times 100$

6 Because of impurities in the sample, or because the crystals may not be dry.

7 Unreacted 2-hydroxybenzoic acid

8 You are likely to have recorded a melting temperature range rather than a single temperature. This is because impurities in the sample cause the solid to melt over a range of temperature rather than sharply at one temperature. The narrower the range and the closer your value to 136 °C, the purer your sample.

ore Practical 1

Recognise and make use of appropriate units in calculations.

Use ratios, fractions and percentages.

Translate information between graphical, numerical and algebraic forms.

Plot two variables from experimental or other data.

ore Practical 2

Understand and use the symbols: $=, <, \ll, \gg, >, \propto, \sim$ and $\rightleftharpoons$.

Substitute numerical values into algebraic equations using appropriate units for physical quantities.

Solve algebraic equations.

ore Practical 3

Recognise and make use of appropriate units in calculations.

Recognise and use expressions in decimal and ordinary form.

Use an appropriate number of significant figures.

Find arithmetic means.

Understand and use the symbols: $=, <, \ll, \gg, >, \sim$ and $\rightleftharpoons$.

Change the subject of an equation.

Substitute numerical values into algebraic equations, using appropriate units for physical quantities.

ore Practical 4

Recognise and make use of appropriate units in calculations.

Recognise and use expressions in decimal and ordinary form.

Use an appropriate number of significant figures.

Find arithmetic means.

Understand and use the symbols: $=, <, \ll, \gg, >, \sim$ and $\rightleftharpoons$.

Change the subject of an equation.

Substitute numerical values into algebraic equations, using appropriate units for physical quantities.

ore Practical 5

Use ratios to construct and balance equations.

ore Practical 6

Use ratios to construct and balance equations.

Use percentages to calculate percentage yield.

ore Practical 7

Recognise and make use of appropriate units in calculations.

ore Practical 8

Recognise and make use of appropriate units in calculations.

Use ratios, fractions and percentages.

Translate information between graphical, numerical and algebraic forms.

Plot two variables from experimental or other data.

Core Practical 9a

- Calculate a rate of change from a graph showing a linear relationship.

Core Practical 9b

- Translate information between graphical, numerical and algebraic forms.
- Plot two variables from experimental or other data.

Core Practical 10

- Use a calculator to work out and use exponential and logarithmic functions.
- Substitute numerical values into algebraic equations using appropriate units for physical quantities.
- Plot two variables from experimental or other data.

Core Practical 11

- Use logarithms in relation to quantities that range over several orders of magnitude.
- Change the subject of an equation.
- Substitute numerical values into algebraic equations using appropriate units for physical quantities.

Core Practical 12

- Substitute numerical values into algebraic equations using appropriate units for physical quantities.

Core Practical 13a

- Change the subject of an equation.
- Substitute numerical values into algebraic equations using appropriate units for physical quantities.

Core Practical 13b

- Recognise and make use of appropriate units in calculations.
- Find arithmetic means.
- Recognise and use expressions in decimal and ordinary form.
- Use an appropriate number of significant figures.
- Change the subject of an equation.
- Substitute numerical values into algebraic equations, using appropriate units for physical quantities.

Core Practical 14

- Use ratios, fractions and percentages.

Core Practical 15

- Recognise and make use of appropriate units in calculations.

Core Practical 16

- Substitute numerical values into algebraic equations using appropriate units for physical quantities.